Maths Explorer

My name is _Muhammad Carin_

_____ .

I am _____8_____ years old.

I go to _Hook junior_ school.

I am _____great_____ at Maths!

Juliet and Charles Snape

Collins

Digit Discovery

Planet Pongo is about to explode! Each alien has a number, and must jump to each of the planets in the order of the arrows, obeying the instructions.

Are they all able to escape?

For example:

$8 \times 3 = 24$

Multiply by 3.

For example:

$2 + 4 = 6$

Add the digits of the product.

NO

YES

Digit discovery 1
Will all the numbers you can see escape if they follow the rules?

Write down your discoveries in a table. Can you spot a pattern? Try some more numbers.

1 × 3	3	0 + 3	3
2 × 3			
3 × 3	9	0 + 9	9
4 × 3	12	1 + 2	3
5 × 5			

1 × 9			
2 × 9			
3 × 9	18	1 + 8	9
4 × 9	27	2 + 7	
5 × 9	36		

Digit discovery 2
Try multiplying by 9 instead of 3 at the first stopover. What happens?

Alien Money

In a café, somewhere in London, two aliens sat drinking tea and eating eccles cakes...

These earth cakes are good!

That's more than I can say for this local money!

What do you mean?

They only have six coins whose value is less than their unit of currency, the pound.

An eccles cake costs 84p but it is impossible to pay that amount without using at least one of the coins twice!

Was the alien correct? Or could they pay for an eccles cake exactly without using any coin twice?

UK coins

| 1p | 2p | 5p | 10p | 20p | 50p |

There are six coins with values under £1.00.

What amounts under £1.00 can be made without using two or more of the same coin?

 + + = 53p

 + + = 35p

4

The aliens were from the planet of Zuton. They arrived back at the
Zuton intergalactic spaceport...

Um!... the journey has made me peckish.

Me, too! Let's get a chocolate bar.

SHOOTING STAR
26 ziddies
MADE IN ZUTON

Martian bar
57 ziddies

GALACTIC SLAB
83 ziddies

OUT OF THIS WORLD
SOLAR SYSTEM
1.01 zut
MADE IN ROX

Using Zuton coins, which of the bars could be paid for without any coin being used more than once?

Zuton coins

1 ziddy   2 ziddies   4 ziddies   8 ziddies   16 ziddies   32 ziddies   64 ziddies

The unit of currency on Zuton is the Zut. The Zut is equal to 100 ziddies. There are coins to the value of 1, 2, 4, 8, 16, 32 and 64 ziddies. Can all the amounts from 1 to 99 ziddies be made without using any Zuton coin twice?

32 + 16 + 4 + 1 = 53 ziddies

32 + 2 + 1 = 35 ziddies

5

Galactic Magic

Yoppus

Xeno

Veno

Unk

Juto

Klack

Luto

Menus

Zuton

anticlockwise

Aliens can read your mind!

Think of a number. Keep it secret.

Count it out around the planets using the alien's instructions.

No matter what number you pick, even before you start, the alien knows which planet you will land on!

The Zuton ability to read human minds is very impressive. But this esp (extra-sensory perception) is really etp (extra-terrestrials pretending). Here's one trick they use at galactic 'get-togethers'. Cover up the 'How to do it' section after you've understood it and then show your friends some ecp (extra-clever performance).

rs

Sel

clockwise

Rox

Quel

Panto

Opie

ud

How to do it

I'm going to turn my back and then I want you to think of a number more than 4 but don't say it.

Start your counting with 'one' at planet Yoppus at the end of the tail. Carry on counting out the number in your head, going from planet to planet, clockwise. If your number takes you right around the circle, keep on going around but **not back along the tail**.

When you have counted up to your number, count it out again **going the other way** (anti-clockwise) starting with the planet next to the one you've landed on. **Don't go up the tail**.

When you have finished, read the name of the planet you have landed on, but don't tell me...

... I can tell **you** that it's ZUTON!

You will always land on Zuton, no matter what number you start with (as long as it is over 4). **Think of another number and try it again.**

Sam Gets Tessellated

We are all familiar with tiling. We find it in bathrooms, kitchens, on fireplaces, walls and floors. The Romans called the small tiles they used for pavements and walls 'tessellae'. Designs made with the same size tiles that fit together without any gaps are called tessellations. This tile of Sam can be used to make a tessellation like the one opposite or you could design your own tile to make your own pattern.

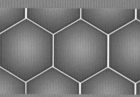

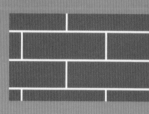

Hexagon tiles and rectangle tile[s] fit together without any gaps.

Will it tessellate?

One way to make a tessellation is to start with a polygon, but be careful, not all polygons tessellate! A polygon is a two-dimensional shape which has three or more straight sides. How many shapes on the right are polygons?

Which of these shapes do you think can be used for tiling without any gaps?

Circles can be used in tessellations if the gaps are turned into shapes and added to the tile:

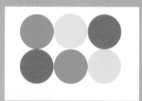

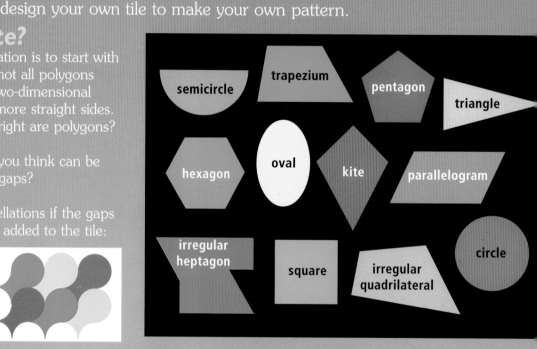

semicircle · trapezium · pentagon · triangle · hexagon · oval · kite · parallelogram · irregular heptagon · square · irregular quadrilateral · circle

Make your own tile to tessellate

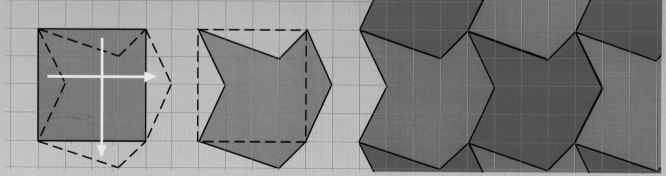

Use cm squared paper. Start by drawing a 4 x 4 square. Take a piece from one side of the square and fit it to the opposite side. Then take another piece from the top and fit it to the bottom. Cut out your new tile carefully. Take another sheet of paper. Draw around the cut-out tile. Now join your cut-out tile to the drawn one so that there is no gap. Trace another tile. Carry on until you have filled the sheet of paper. Complete[ ] your design with two different colours.

Making a 'Sam' tile

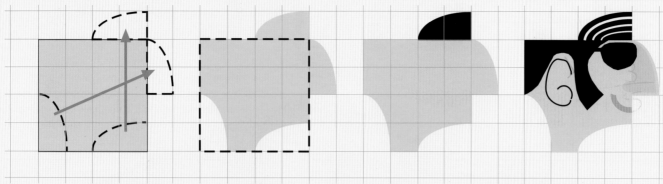

This 'Sam' tile also slots together to make a tessellation. Starting with a square, pieces are cut out from one side and added to the opposite sides to make his nose and hair.

(If you make a tile with curves, it may be easier to trace and repeat, rather than make a cut-out template.)

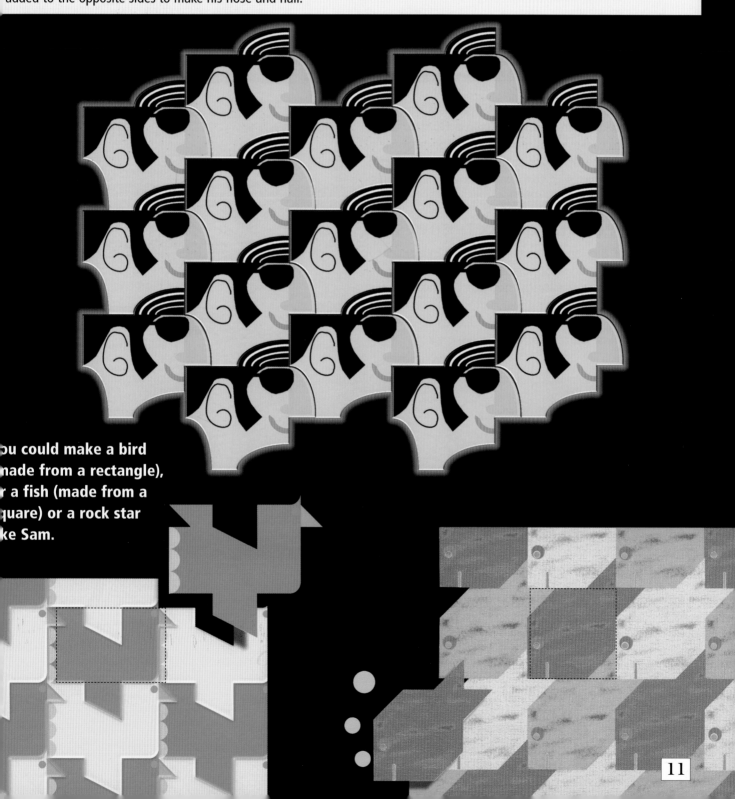

ou could make a bird
made from a rectangle),
r a fish (made from a
quare) or a rock star
ke Sam.

Measuring Greeks

The first simple measures of length used fingers, spans, feet, elbows and other parts of the human body.

This drawing is based on the 'metrological man' in the Ashmolean Museum, Oxford. The marble carving was made by the Ancient Greeks. It may have been used to check traders' measures or as a decoration above a trader's office.

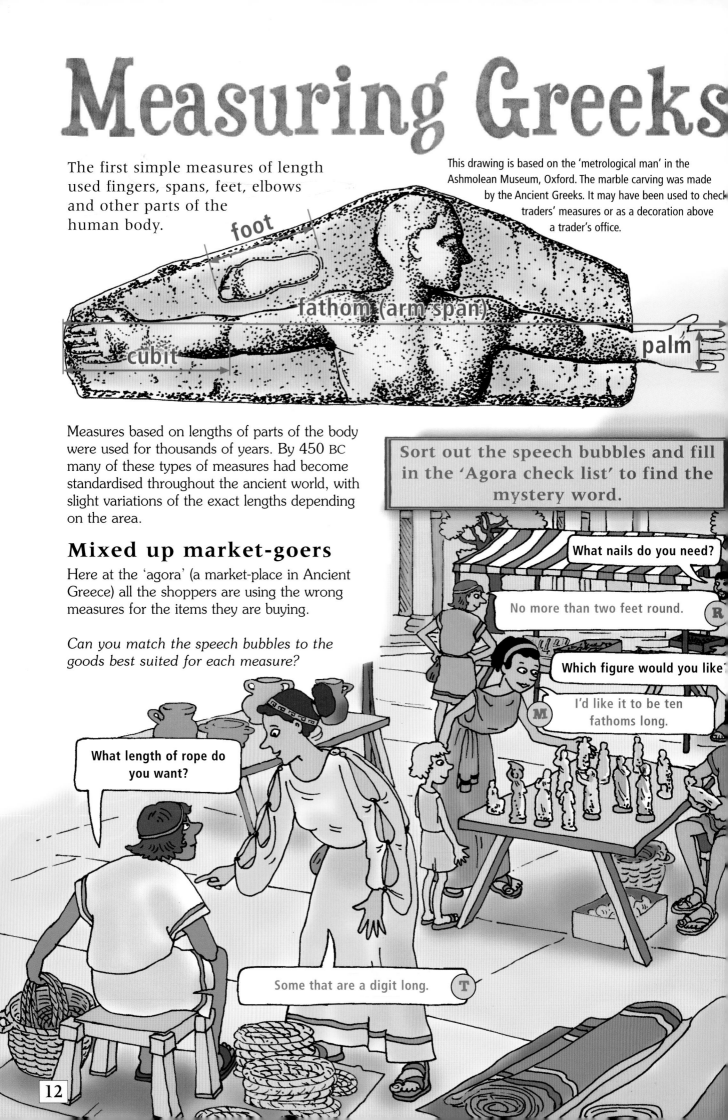

foot

fathom (arm span)

cubit

palm

Measures based on lengths of parts of the body were used for thousands of years. By 450 BC many of these types of measures had become standardised throughout the ancient world, with slight variations of the exact lengths depending on the area.

Mixed up market-goers

Here at the 'agora' (a market-place in Ancient Greece) all the shoppers are using the wrong measures for the items they are buying.

Can you match the speech bubbles to the goods best suited for each measure?

Sort out the speech bubbles and fill in the 'Agora check list' to find the mystery word.

What nails do you need?

No more than two feet round. **R**

Which figure would you like?

I'd like it to be ten fathoms long. **M**

What length of rope do you want?

Some that are a digit long. **T**

Greek measures

Greek measure		Measure in centimetres
Digit	(width of a finger)	1.85
Palm	(width of 4 digits)	7.4
Span	(width of 12 digits)	22.2
Foot	(width of 16 digits)	29.6
Cubit	(width of 24 digits)	44.4
Fathom	(length of 6 feet)	177.6

Most of the Greek standard measures were well known in the ancient world. Many examples can be found in the Bible. Noah's Ark was 300 cubits long and the giant warrior Goliath was 6 cubits and a span tall.

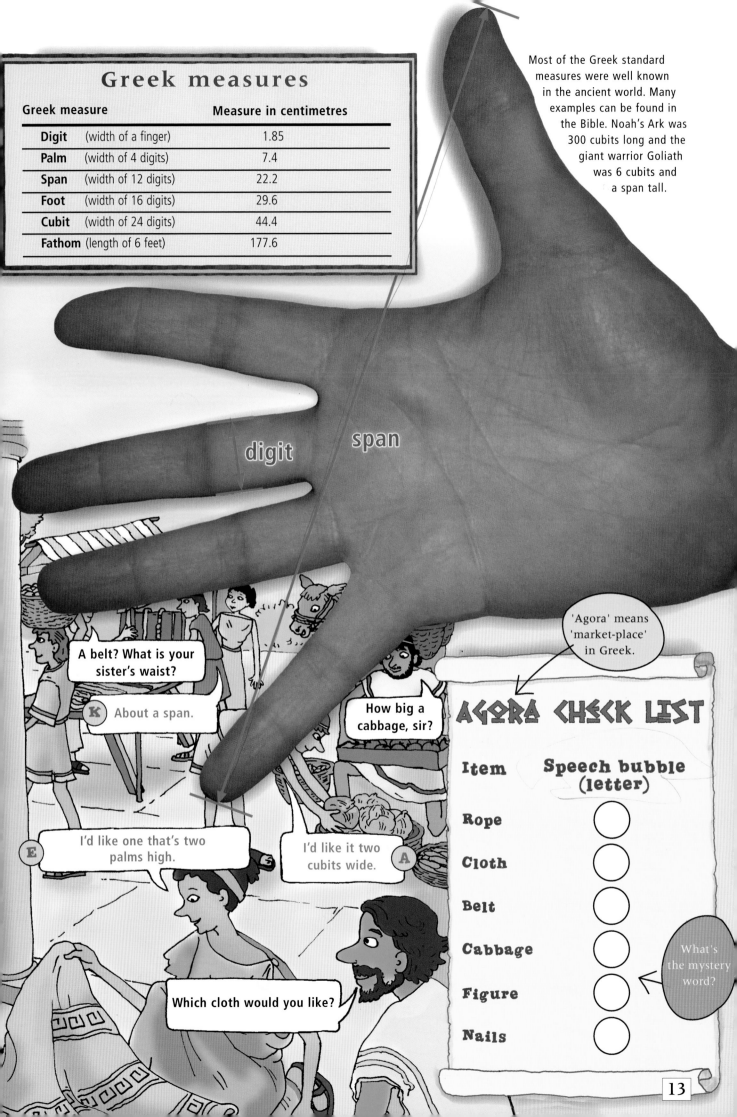

digit

span

A belt? What is your sister's waist?

K About a span.

How big a cabbage, sir?

'Agora' means 'market-place' in Greek.

AGORA CHECK LIST

E I'd like one that's two palms high.

I'd like it two cubits wide. **A**

Which cloth would you like?

Item	Speech bubble (letter)
Rope	◯
Cloth	◯
Belt	◯
Cabbage	◯
Figure	◯
Nails	◯

What's the mystery word?

COLOSSUS
the sixth wonder of the world!

Between 304 BC and 282 BC the people of the Greek island of Rhodes built an extraordinary statue of polished metal of their sun god, Helios. They called it Colossus (the Greek word for gigantic). Standing proudly at the entrance to the harbour, the shiny bronze figure became one of the Wonders of the World.

Only fifty-eight years later an earthquake shook the island. The statue broke at the knees and Colossus came crashing down, smashing into pieces.

Pliny, a famous Roman writer, saw the ruins about 250 years later. He wrote, 'few men can clasp the thumb in their arms, and its fingers are larger than most statues.'

Seven hundred years later the pieces of Colossus were taken away and sold for scrap metal. It took 900 camels to transport them.

It's a colossal earthquake!

Help!

Arrgh!

Wow! The thumb's circumference is the same as my arm span

PLINY

Where is this great statue, then?

Cor, that's big!

It's colossal!

Height and arm span

Did you know that the height of a person and the length of their arm span are more or less the same?

ow tall was Colossus?

egend has it that Colossus stood as high as a mountain but nothing now remains of the giant tatue. Yet, using what Pliny told us, that a man's **rm span** (a fathom) was equal to the circumference of Colossus' thumb, you can work out his height.

1. Measure around your own thumb to find its circumference. Use a strip of paper and mark it.

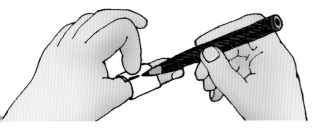

2. Put the marked piece of paper against the length of your thumb. What do you notice?

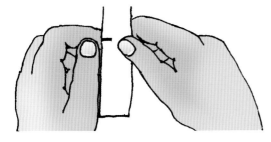

3. Use your paper measure to find out how many thumb-lengths are in your arm span.

Can you work out the height of Colossus using this information?

Hint: See the table on page 13 to find out the ength of a man's arm span (a fathom) in centimetres, and look at the diagram at the op of this page.)

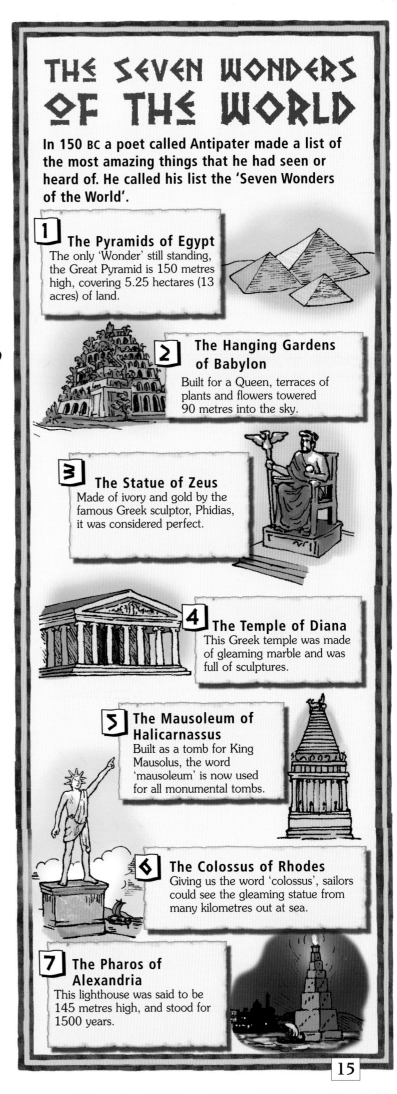

THE SEVEN WONDERS OF THE WORLD

In 150 BC a poet called Antipater made a list of the most amazing things that he had seen or heard of. He called his list the 'Seven Wonders of the World'.

1 The Pyramids of Egypt
The only 'Wonder' still standing, the Great Pyramid is 150 metres high, covering 5.25 hectares (13 acres) of land.

2 The Hanging Gardens of Babylon
Built for a Queen, terraces of plants and flowers towered 90 metres into the sky.

3 The Statue of Zeus
Made of ivory and gold by the famous Greek sculptor, Phidias, it was considered perfect.

4 The Temple of Diana
This Greek temple was made of gleaming marble and was full of sculptures.

5 The Mausoleum of Halicarnassus
Built as a tomb for King Mausolus, the word 'mausoleum' is now used for all monumental tombs.

6 The Colossus of Rhodes
Giving us the word 'colossus', sailors could see the gleaming statue from many kilometres out at sea.

7 The Pharos of Alexandria
This lighthouse was said to be 145 metres high, and stood for 1500 years.

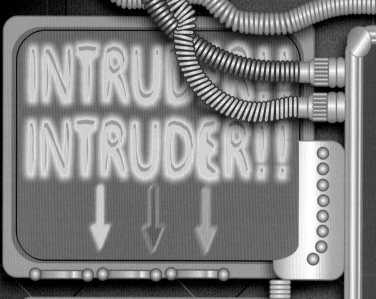

INTRUDER
INTRUDER!!

The spacecraft are waiting to land. One of the craft is an intruder — but which one?

The controller must find out ... and quickly.

Each craft has an identity number. A correct number can be made using multiples of 3 and 20.

e.g. 44 = 1 x 20 plus 8 x 3

The identity number of the intruder craft can't be made in this way. What's the number of the intruder's craft?

Use the 3 and 20 times tables on the right if you need help.

ENTER

CLOSE

The numbers on the spaceships: 181, 67, 32, 79, 37, 47, 167, 26

×		
1	3	20
2		
3	9	60
4	12	80
5	15	100
6	18	120
7	21	140
8	24	160
9	27	180
10	30	200

Intruder Investigation

⬤ Which numbers under 100 can you make
using only multiples of 3 and 20?
Making a table will help.

⬤ Which numbers can't you make?

Shrink that Shape

It's easy to make a shape smaller and smaller – here's how!

You will need a pencil, ruler, paper and colouring pens.

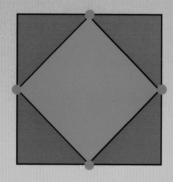

Draw a square (about 8 cm x 8 cm) and mark a point at the centre of each side. Join the points to make a smaller square inside the first one.

How much smaller is the second square than the first?

Mark centre points in this smaller square and join them up.

Carry on doing this, getting smaller and smaller until you have got too small to do any more.

Try starting with regular shapes like triangles (3-sided shapes), hexagons (6-sided shapes) or other rectangles (4-sided shapes). *How would you describe what happens to rectangles that are not squares?*

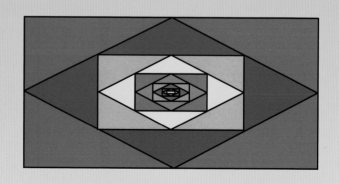

18

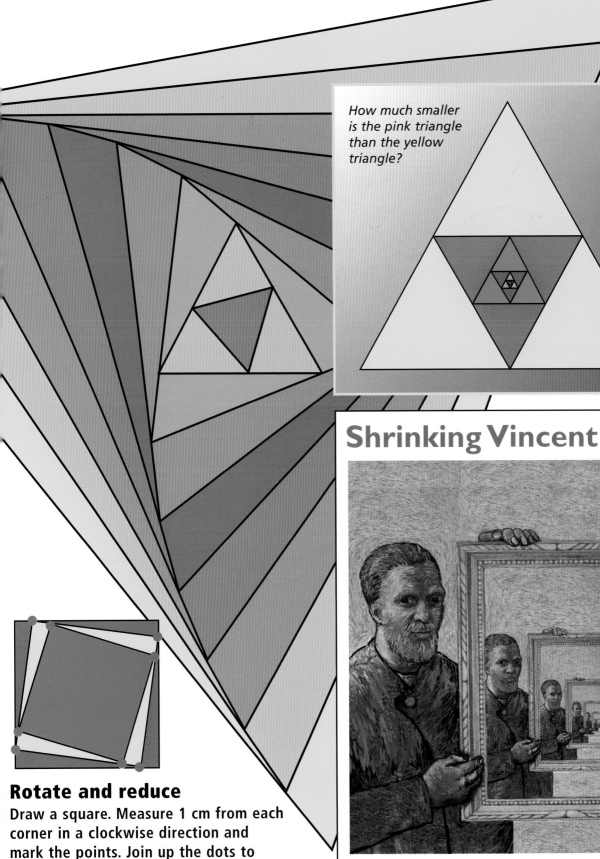

How much smaller is the pink triangle than the yellow triangle?

Rotate and reduce

Draw a square. Measure 1 cm from each corner in a clockwise direction and mark the points. Join up the dots to make another smaller square.

Keep on measuring and joining until you can't get any smaller.

Try other starting shapes.

Shrinking Vincent

Vincent is looking at a mirror whilst holding another mirror. This makes a reflection that gets smaller and smaller. Each reflection is reduced to half the height. *If all the reflections of Vincent in the mirror were piled on top of each other would they be as tall as the real Vincent?*

Billy's bathtime

Use the graph of Billy's bathtime story opposite to put the events below in order. One is done for you.

			Correct order	Check letters
Billy reads a magazine.	I to J		9	L
Billy gets in the bath.	to			C
Billy pulls the plug.	to			Y
Billy lies down.	to			E
Billy sits up again.	to			I
Billy fills the bath.	to			A
Billy holds his breath.	to			B
Billy washes.	to			L
Billy ducks under the water.	to			N
Billy floats his feet.	to			A
Billy gets out of the bath.	to			L

Did you get the events in the correct order? Fill in the boxes below with the check letters. What does it say?

1	2	3	4	5	6	7	8	9	10	11

Would a graph of your bath differ from Billy's?

Take a careful look at the story of Billy's bathtime shown below as a graph. The vertical axis shows how the depth of water changes and the horizontal axis shows time.

Billy's bathtime story

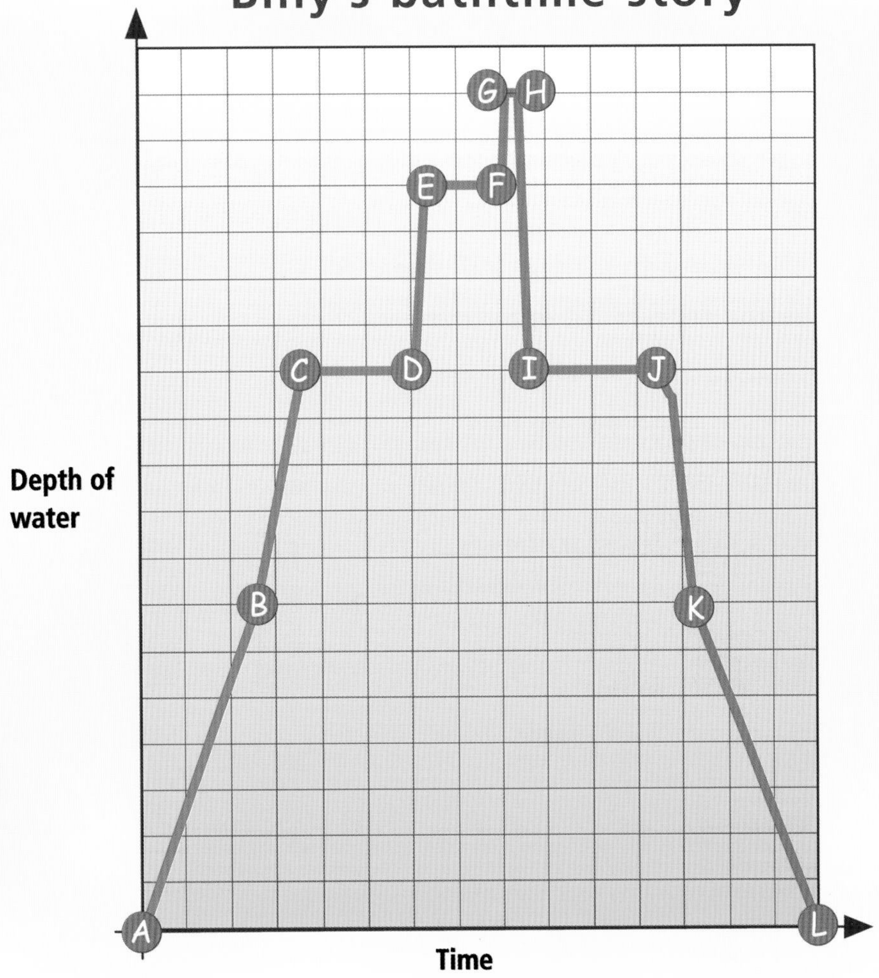

Depth of water

Time

Other stories... other graphs

These are graphs of more of Billy's activities. Match the graph to the activity and choose the correct label for the y-axis.

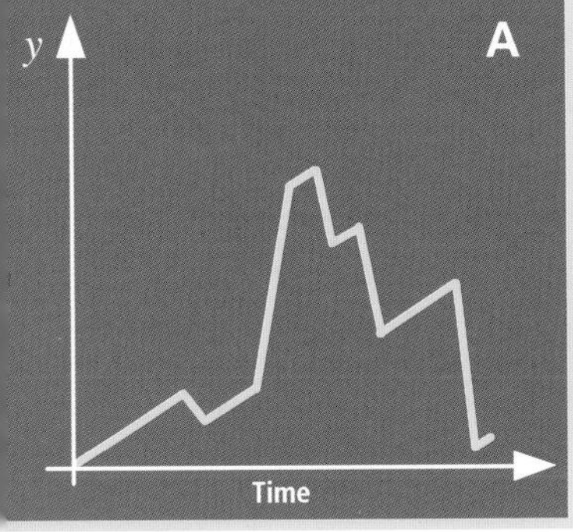

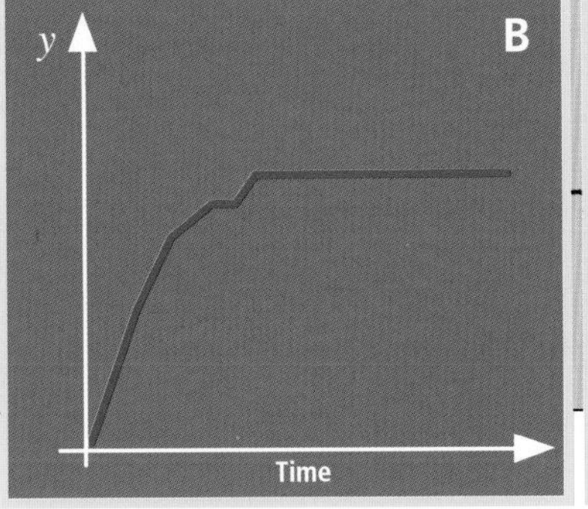

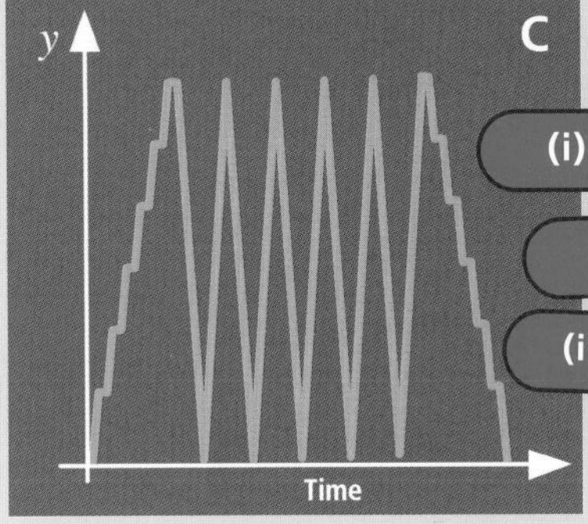

(1) Billy climbs a hill.

(2) Billy's money box over a year.

(3) Billy goes on the big wheel.

A

B

C

Time

Time

Time

(i) Height of carriage

(ii) Height up hill

(iii) Amount of money

USE YOUR HEAD to see 3D

How good are you at visualising? Take a look at these plans and nets below. Picture what they would look like if you cut along the bold black lines and folded the dotted lines.

You don't need scissors or paper – just your head!

Paper cuts and folds

Can you match these 2D plans to the correct 3D drawings?

——— means cut

·············· means fold

Match the letters by each 3D drawing to these plans to see what you used to do this!

(1) (2) (3) (4) (5) (6) (7) (8) (9) (10)

1	
2	
3	
4	
5	
6	
7	
8	
9	
10	

P A

R E

O R

N B

W I

and spot the cubes.

A net is a two-dimensional (2D) plan that can be folded to make a three-dimensional (3D) model of a solid.

Folding cubes

There are many ways to arrange a net of six squares to make a cube.

Only five of these nets will make cubes when you fold them along the dotted lines. Can you visualise which ones by making them in your head?

U   C   B   O

X   A   H   E

S   P

You could cut and fold squared paper to test if you are right.

What word can you make with the five letters of the correct nets?

23

PRIME NUMBERS have intrigued and puzzled mathematicians for thousands of years. What are they and how do you find them?

Prime Time

What is a prime number?

A number that cannot be divided exactly by any other whole number without a remainder (other than 1 and, of course, itself) is a **prime number**.

20 can be divided exactly by 2, 4, 5 and 10. The numbers that can be used to divide **20** are called factors. **20** has four factors (not including 1 and itself).

29 has no factors except 1 and itself. So **29** is a prime number.

In about 250 BC the librarian of the Library of Alexandria was the mathematician Eratosthenes. It was the largest library the world had ever seen.
It contained more than 800 000 handwritten scrolls.

Let's go for a scroll.

Any new primes, Eratosthenes?

How do I know 23 is a prime number?

Because 23 can only be divided, without a remainder, by itself and

Numbers are tested to see if they can be divided by any other whole number.

A number that has no factors other than 1 and itself are prime.

All numbers that aren't prime are called composite numbers.

So, why isn't 21 a prime number?

It can be divided by 3 and by 7 without a remainder.

LOVELY PRIMES

24

The mathematical sieve

One of the first mathematicians to try to get to grips with prime numbers was Eratosthenes who lived in Alexandria, in Egypt.

Eratosthenes devised a 'mathematical sieve'; any numbers that didn't fall through the sieve were prime.

Eratosthenes' sieve

How to use the prime number sieve

1. The number 1 is not a prime number. Cross it out.

2. The number 2 is the only prime number that is even. Draw a circle around it and then cross out every second number, that's all even numbers (4, 6, 8, 10, ...).

3. 3 is also a prime number. Draw a circle around it and then cross out every third number (6, 9, 12, 15, ...) because they are all multiples of 3.

4. The number 4 is crossed out because it is a multiple of 2. The next number not crossed out is 5. This is the next prime number. Circle it, then cross out every fifth number (10, 15, 20, 25, ...).

5. Carry on to the next number that hasn't been crossed out and continue in the same way.

Can you use the sieve to find all the prime numbers up to 100?

A number 18 miles long!

$$2^{13466917} - 1$$

This prime number is written in the shortened form used by mathematicians. It means 1 less than $2 \times 2 \times 2$ ... multiplied by itself more than 13 million times. The strip along the top of the page shows the beginning of the number. Written out in full in a single line it would contain over 4 million digits and it would be 28.5 kilometres long (nearly 18 miles)!

The largest prime number

The Ancient Greeks proved long ago that no matter how large a prime number is there will always be larger prime numbers.

The sieve of Eratosthenes is still the best way to find prime numbers under 1 000 000 but, beyond this, mathematicians use computers that run programs based on number work by Lagrange (an eighteenth-century Italian mathematician).

Prime patterns

By putting numbers in a 6-column grid certain patterns occur. Copy this grid and extend it up to about 150. *What patterns can you find in the columns and diagonals?*

1	2	3	4	5	6
7	8	9	10	11	12
13	14	15	16	17	18
19	20	21	22	23	24
25	26	27	28	29	30
31	32	33	34	35	36
37	38	39	40	41	42
43	44	45	46	47	48

25

Russian Multiplication

People have always found multiplying hard, especially in the days before electronic calculators were invented. The Ancient Egyptians used a way of multiplying by doubling. This method was passed on through time and to different peoples. It was widely used by the country people of Russia until halfway through the twentieth century.

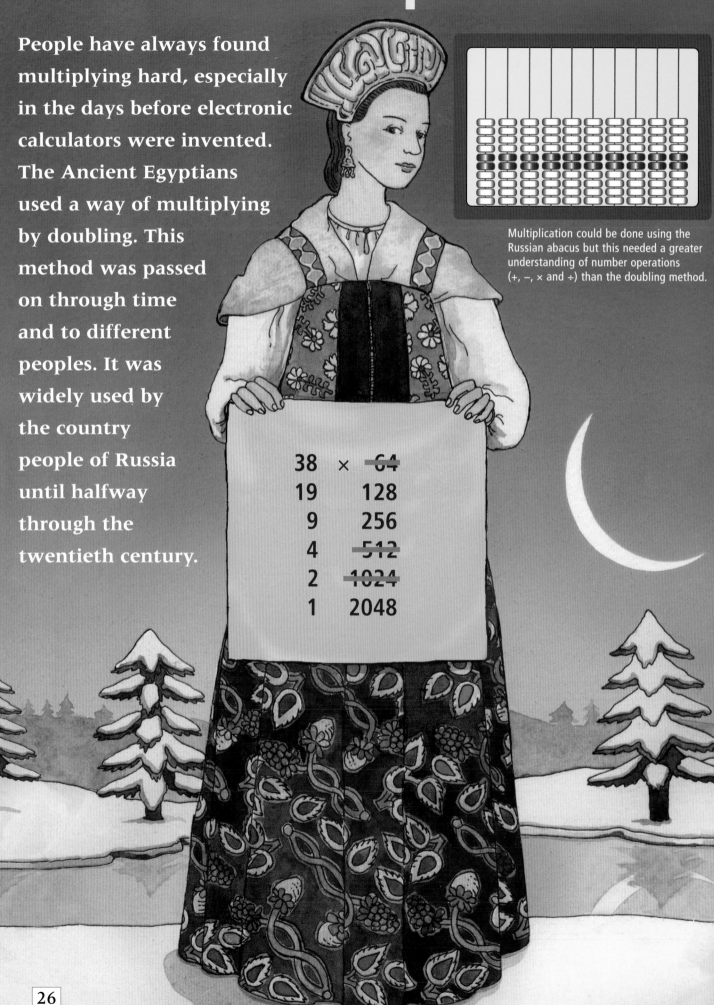

Multiplication could be done using the Russian abacus but this needed a greater understanding of number operations (+, −, × and ÷) than the doubling method.

38	×	64
19		128
9		256
4		512
2		1024
1		2048

Doing Russian multiplication

With this Russian method of multiplying you only need to double, halve and add. Here's how to do 38 × 64...

	Halve the numbers in this column	Double the numbers in this column	
At the top of your paper write the multiplication.	38	×	~~64~~	
Halve the number on the left and double the number on the right.	19	128	→ 128
If the halving results in a half, go to the next lowest whole number.	9	256	→ 256
Carry on halving and doubling until you get to 1 in the left column.	4	~~512~~	
Now cross out any numbers in the right column that are opposite an even number in the left column.	2	~~1024~~	
	1	2048	→ 2048

> Add ONLY the numbers in the right column that are opposite an odd number in the left column.

Add the remaining numbers to get the total.

$$38 × 64 = 2432$$

Does it matter if you do the multiplication with the numbers swapped around?

$$64 × 38$$

If there was an odd number in the multiplication, would it be better to have it in the left column or the right, or doesn't it matter?

Which are right?

Here are three multiplications done the Russian way. One of them is **not** correct!
Can you work out which it is? Can you spot the mistakes?

A

358	×	~~16~~
178		~~32~~
89		64
42		~~128~~
21		256
10		~~512~~
5		1024
2		~~2048~~
1		4096
		5440

B

44	×	~~22~~
22		~~44~~
11		88
5		176
2		~~352~~
1		704
		968

C

29	×	6
14		~~12~~
7		24
3		48
1		96
		174

Paper cranes for peace

Sadako Sasaki, a young girl who lived in Hiroshima, Japan, was only two years old when in 1945 an atom bomb was dropped on the city.

Fortunately, Sadako and her family survived the massive blast and the following firestorm. As time passed Sadako started school, becoming a strong runner. But when she was 12 years old, just after she had won the relay race at her sports day, she fell ill. Sadako had leukaemia, often described as 'the atom bomb disease'.

Her friend Chizuko visited her in hospital, bringing a gift of squares of gold-sided paper. She told Sadako about the legend that a wish might be granted if 1000 paper cranes were made. Sadako began to make hundreds of paper cranes, getting much pleasure and hope from seeing them hanging all around her room.

Despite her positive spirit, she only managed to make 644 cranes before she died. Sadako's school friends wanted to complete the 1000 paper cranes. They began folding cranes and raising money so that a statue could be put up remembering all the children that had been affected by the bomb.

Today that statue stands in Hiroshima's 'Peace Park' with the words:

'This is our cry,
This is our prayer,
Peace in the world.'

Paper cranes from all around the world are sent here each year, as a symbol of peace.

Folding

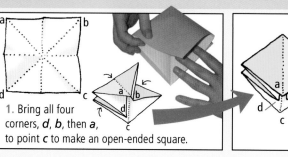

The secret

The crane is not the easiest origami model to make but you'll be fine if you follow the instructions carefully. It is important to note when to fold layers separately, turn OVER the model to do the back layer, and to press down firmly. Always line up edges neatly! Dotted lines represent fold or crease lines.

Use a 20 cm square of thin paper (origami paper is coloured on one side). **Prepare** the square by folding it diagonally into triangles and then horizontally and vertically into rectangles as in diagrams (A) to (G) on the right. Open up the paper each time to create accurate crease marks as shown in diagram (G).

1. Bring all four corners, *d*, *b*, then *a*, to point *c* to make an open-ended square.

4. Unfold to see all the crease lines you have made.

5. Lift the top layer at point *c* and fold back along hinge *ef* to make a large diamond shape which opens in the centre. Press flat. **Turn over** and do the same thing to the other layer.

8. Lift the top layer and **fold over** from the right (like turning the page of a book). **Turn over** and do the same on the other side.

Your shape now has two split triangular points at one end (like ears) and a long triangular shape (like a nose) at the other.

11. Bring down the 'wings', gently pulling them out.

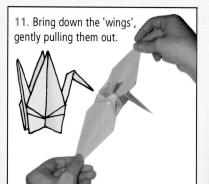

12. Look underneath your model to find a small hole, and gently blow into it to puff out the body.

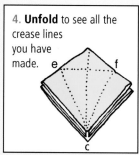

Geometry

lding cranes

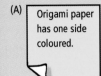

(A) Origami paper has one side coloured.

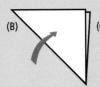

(B) (C)

 (E) 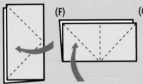 (F) (G)

Open out the square after each fold so that creases will be neat and accurate.

2. Take only the upper layer of the right-hand side and **fold** into the centre along fold-line *fc*, and **fold** in the top layer of the left-hand side along fold-line *ec*.

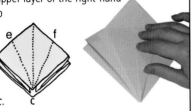

3. Now turn over and do the same to the other side. Then fold down the top triangle along fold line *fe*.

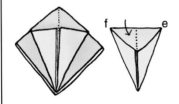

6. You should now have a diamond shape with a split bottom half.

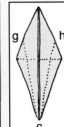

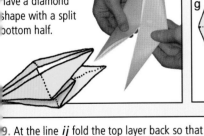

7. Taking the top layer **fold** in each side at fold lines *gc* and *hc* so that they meet along the centre line. Turn over and do the same to the other side. This makes an even thinner diamond shape.

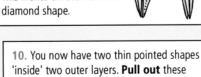

9. At the line *ij* fold the top layer back so that the point of the 'nose' meets the points of the 'ears' (at *k*). Turn over and repeat. '**Book fold**' (as you did at stage 8) the top right-hand layer (from *j* to *i*), then **turn over** and do the same on the other side.

10. You now have two thin pointed shapes 'inside' two outer layers. **Pull out** these to the positions shown. They are the crane's head and tail.

Press in the tip of one of these pointed shapes to make the head shape.

13. Well done! You have made the famous origami model of the crane, known all over the world as Sadako's 'symbol of peace'.

'I will write 'peace' on your wings, and you will fly all over the world.'

Sadako Sasaki

Geometry and ORIGAMI

The Japanese have been folding fantastic paper models for hundreds of years. They call the art of paper folding 'origami'. This word comes from the Japanese *oru* which means 'paper' and *kami* which means 'fold'.

Mathematicians have found that origami can be used to show complicated geometric shapes. If you undo your origami model you will see that you have folded many polygons, including different types of triangles and quadrilaterals.

Paper folding can be used to prove geometric rules. Here's an example:

The angles in a triangle sum to 180°.

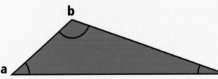

1. Cut out any triangle.

2. Fold down angle b (the top corner) so that it touches the opposite side. Make sure the fold is **parallel** to the base.

3. Fold in angles a and c to meet b.

4. The three angles form a straight line along the base. The angle of a straight line is 180°. Therefore the angles in a triangle sum to 180°.

Solutions

This is where you can check your answers, or see how to solve a puzzle if you've got stuck. At the end of each we tell you which part of the Maths curriculum you're practising.

Digit Discovery (pages 2 and 3)

All the numbers shown can escape. In fact, all numbers, no matter how large, could escape! They will all reduce down to 3, 6 or 9 after visiting the planets enough times.

Digit discovery 1
Adding the digits of the product (on the second planet) gives you a digital root. The right-hand column of your table lists the digital roots of the **3 times table**. The repeating pattern in this column is 3, 6, 9, 3, 6, 9 etc.

Digit discovery 2
The digital root of any product of the **9 times table** is always 9. You should be able to see this in the right-hand column of your table.

Maths topic: Calculations, number properties

Alien Money (pages 4 and 5)

UK coins
You can't make 4p or 9p or any amount with 4 or 9 in it without using two coins of the same value.

Zuton coins
You can make all the amounts from 1 to 99 ziddies without using any Zuton coin twice. You can buy all the chocolate bars without using any coin more than once:

Shooting Star   16 + 8 + 2 = 26 ziddies
Martian Bar   32 + 16 + 8 + 1 = 57 ziddies
Galactic Slab   64 + 16 + 2 + 1 = 83 ziddies
Solar System   64 + 32 + 4 + 1 = 101 ziddies = 1.01 Zut

Maths topic: Numbers and the number system, calculations

Galactic Magic (pages 6 and 7)

If your chosen number is larger than 4, you will always land on Zuton because it is 5 planets away from Tars which is 5 planets away from the start.

For example: you choose number 9. Count 5 to get to Tars and then another 4 to make 9 (you land on Panto). Then count 9 anticlockwise, not going up the tail.

When you get to Tars you will have counted 4 and then there are 5 more planets to get to Zuton.

Maths topic: Solving problems

Get off the Island (pages 8 and 9)

Will all the numbers shown escape?
All the numbers you can see on the island can escape. They all eventually reduce down to 1. This is the escape route for number 7:

$7 \rightarrow 22 \rightarrow 11 \rightarrow 34 \rightarrow 17 \rightarrow 52 \rightarrow 26 \rightarrow 13 \rightarrow 40 \rightarrow 20 \rightarrow 10 \rightarrow 5 \rightarrow 16 \rightarrow 8 \rightarrow 4 \rightarrow 2 \rightarrow 1 \rightarrow$ **ESCAPE**

You can use this escape route as a shortcut to get the other numbers off the island. Just look for where the number in your calculation occurs in this list.

Numbers that are powers of 2 can get off the island quickest:
$2 \times 2 =$ **4**
$2 \times 2 \times 2 =$ **8**
$2 \times 2 \times 2 \times 2 =$ **16**
$2 \times 2 \times 2 \times 2 \times 2 =$ **32**

Can any number escape?
All numbers can escape. 256, which is a power of 2, will get off the island much quicker than 156 which isn't (156 takes 30 stages before reducing down to 16).

Maths topic: Calculations

Sam Gets Tessellated (pages 10 and 11)

Will it tessellate?
There are 9 polygons (the semicircle, oval and circle don't have three straight sides). Six of the polygons can be used for tiling without any gaps: triangle, hexagon, kite, parallelogram, square and the trapezium (with rotations).

Maths topic: Measures, shape and space

Measuring Greeks
(pages 12 and 13)

Agora check list

Item	Speech bubble letter	Units
Rope	M	Fathoms
Cloth	A	Cubits
Belt	R	Feet
Cabbage	K	Span
Figure	E	Palms
Nails	T	Digits

The mystery word is 'MARKET'.

Maths topic: Measures, shape and space

Colossus (pages 14 and 15)

By measuring your thumb, you will find that its length and its circumference are about the same. Page 15 tells us that a person's arm span is roughly equal to their height. Count how many times your thumb-length goes into your arm span. It will probably be about 24 times.

Pliny's arm span (and Colossus' thumb) is about a fathom (177.6 cm or 1.776 m), which is approximately 1.8 m (using the Greek measures table on page 13).

To find out Colossus' height, multiply Pliny's arm span in metres by 24:
1.8 m × 24 = 43.2 m.
Round this to 43 m.

Maths topic: Calculations, measures, shape and space

Intruder Investigation (pages 16 and 17)

The intruder's spacecraft is number **37**. All other numbers can be made using multiples of 3 and 20:

50 =	1 × 20	+	10 × 3
26 =	1 × 20	+	2 × 3
65 =	1 × 20	+	15 × 3
167 =	7 × 20	+	9 × 3
253 =	11 × 20	+	11 × 3
47 =	1 × 20	+	9 × 3
32 =	1 × 20	+	4 × 3
79 =	2 × 20	+	13 × 3
181 =	8 × 20	+	7 × 3
67 =	2 × 20	+	9 × 3

1 to 100
Between 1 and 19 the only multiples of 3 that can be made are 3, 6, 9, 12, 15 and 18. Using multiples of 3 and 20, all the numbers between 20 and 100 can be made except 22, 25, 31, 34 and 37.

Maths topic: Calculations, multiplying and order of operations

Shrink that Shape (pages 18 and 19)

(page 18) The second **square** is half the area of the first square. The third square has sides which are half the length of the first square. Alternate squares are a quarter of one another in length and a quarter of one another in area.

With **rectangles** the second shape made is a rhombus (all sides equal and opposite sides parallel) which has half the area of the first shape (the rectangle). The third shape is a rectangle and its sides are half the length of the first rectangle.

(Page 19 top) The pink **triangle** is a quarter of the area of the yellow triangle and its sides are half the length. The pattern is the same for the next (blue) triangle and the next and so on.

Diagrams not to scale.

(Page 19 bottom) **Shrinking Vincent**
The lengths in the reflections are all half of those in the previous one. The piled up measurements can be shown like this:
$$\frac{1}{2} + \frac{1}{4} + \frac{1}{8} + \frac{1}{16} + \ldots$$
The reflections piled on top of one another will not be as tall as the real Vincent – they will always be a 'fraction' shorter.

Maths topic: Measures, shape and space, fractions

Billy's Bathtime (pages 20 and 21)

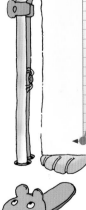

Event	From	To	Correct order
Reads	I	J	9
Gets in bath	B	C	2
Pulls plug	K	L	11
Lies down	D	E	4
Sits up	H	I	8
Fills bath	A	B	1
Holds breath	G	H	7
Washes	C	D	3
Ducks under	F	G	6
Floats feet	E	F	5
Gets out	J	K	10

The check letters should read: A CLEAN BILLY

Other stories... other graphs

Graph	Title	y-axis
A	2	(iii)
B	1	(ii)
C	3	(i)

Maths topic: Handling data, reasoning

Use Your Head (pages 22 and 23)

Paper cuts and folds

1	B
2	R
3	A
4	I
5	N
6	P
7	O
8	W
9	E
10	R

Folding cubes

B	O	X	E	S

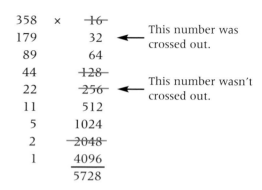

Maths topic: Measures, shape and space

Prime Time (pages 24 and 25)

Prime numbers under 100
2, 3, 5, 7, 11, 13, 17, 19, 23, 29, 31, 37, 41, 43, 47, 53, 59, 61, 67, 71, 73, 79, 83, 89, 97

Prime patterns
Prime numbers greater than 3 always fall in the columns headed 1 and 5 in a six-column grid. All primes greater than 3 are 1 less or 1 more than a multiple of 6.

Maths topic: Numbers and the number system

Russian Multiplication (pages 26 and 27)

It doesn't matter which way round you do the multiplication or which column you have the odd number in – you will still get the same answer.

A is wrong. It should be:

358	×	~~16~~	
179		32	← This number was crossed out.
89		64	
44		~~128~~	
22		~~256~~	← This number wasn't crossed out.
11		512	
5		1024	
2		~~2048~~	
1		4096	
		5728	

Maths topic: Numbers and the number system

Folding Geometry (pages 28 and 29)

Most origami models are not easy to do so don't worry if it takes you ages to make the crane. Follow the instructions and diagrams carefully and you'll be fine. Ask someone else for help if you get stuck.

Maths topic: Measures, shape and space

Published by Collins
An imprint of HarperCollins*Publishers*
77 – 85 Fulham Palace Road
Hammersmith
London
W6 8JB

Browse the complete Collins catalogue at
www.collins.co.uk

© 2005 Juliet and Charles Snape

10 9 8 7 6 5 4 3 2 1

ISBN 0 00 721146 5

Juliet and Charles Snape assert their moral rights to be identified as the authors of this work

British Library Cataloguing in Publication Data
A Catalogue record for this publication is available from the British Library

Written by Juliet and Charles Snape
Consultant: Nigel Langdon MPhil, a maths consultant for the Royal Borough of Kingston upon Thames
Design, cover and illustrations by Juliet and Charles Snape
Printed and bound by Imago Thailand

Titles in this series:
Maths Explorer, Maths Mazes, Maths Mysteries, Maths Puzzles
To order any of these titles, please telephone **0870 787 1732** and quote code **256V**.